New Framework Maths

Word Problems
Year 6

By Richard Cooper

This book is not photocopiable.

Rising Stars UK Ltd., 22 Grafton Street, London
W1S 4EX

www.risingstars-uk.com

First edition published 2003
This edition published 2007
Reprinted 2008
Text, design and layout © Rising Stars UK Ltd.
Editorial consultant: Caroline Cooke
Design and illustration: Redmoor Design, Tavistock,
Devon

British Library Cataloguing in Publication Data

A CIP record for this book is available from the
British Library.

ISBN 978-1-84680-217-1

Printed by Craft Print International Ltd., Singapore

Contents

Coverage of Primary National Strategy Objectives

	Using and applying mathematics					**Counting and understanding number**					**Knowing and using number facts**				**Calculating**
	Solve multi-step problems, and problems involving fractions, decimals and percentages; choose and use appropriate calculation strategies at each stage, including calculator use	Tabulate systematically the information in a problem or puzzle; identify and record the steps or calculations needed to solve it, using symbols where appropriate; interpret solutions in the original context and check their accuracy	Suggest, plan and develop lines of enquiry; collect, organise and represent information, interpret results and review methods; identify and answer related questions	Represent and interpret sequences, patterns and relationships involving numbers and shapes; suggest and test hypotheses; construct and use simple expressions and formulae in words then symbols (e.g. the cost of c pens at 15 pence each is $15c$ pence)	Explain reasoning and conclusions, using words, symbols or diagrams as appropriate	Find the difference between a positive and a negative integer, or two negative integers, in context	Use decimal notation for tenths, hundredths and thousandths; partition, round and order decimals with up to three places, and position them on the number line	Express a larger whole number as a fraction of a smaller one (e.g. recognise that 8 slices of a 5-slice pizza represents $8/5$ or $1\tfrac{3}{5}$ pizzas); simplify fractions by cancelling common factors; order a set of fractions by converting them to fractions with a common denominator	**Express one quantity as a percentage of another (e.g. express £400 as a percentage of £1000); find equivalent percentages, decimals and fractions**	Solve simple problems involving direct proportion by scaling quantities up or down	**Use knowledge of place value and multiplication facts to 10 × 10 to derive related multiplication and division facts involving decimals (e.g. 0.8 × 7, 4.8 ÷ 6)**	Use knowledge of multiplication facts to derive quickly squares of numbers to 12 × 12 and the corresponding squares of multiples of 10	Recognise that prime numbers have only two factors and identify prime numbers less than 100; find the prime factors of two-digit whole numbers	Use approximations, inverse operations and tests of divisibility to estimate and check results	Calculate mentally with integers and decimals: U.t ± U.t, TU × U, TU ÷ U, U.t × U, U.t ÷ U
Place value	✓													✓	
Fractions	✓													✓	✓
Decimals	✓	✓					✓						✓	✓	✓
Percentages	✓												✓	✓	✓
Addition	✓	✓											✓	✓	✓
Subtraction	✓	✓											✓	✓	✓
Money	✓	✓											✓	✓	✓
Time	✓	✓											✓	✓	✓
Measures	✓	✓					✓						✓	✓	✓
Puzzles	✓	✓			✓							✓	✓	✓	✓
Patterns and sequences	✓			✓									✓	✓	✓
Multiplication	✓	✓									✓		✓	✓	✓
Division	✓	✓								✓	✓		✓	✓	✓
2D shapes	✓	✓			✓										
3D shapes	✓	✓		✓	✓										
Position and direction	✓	✓													
Data handling	✓	✓	✓												
Two-step problems	✓	✓													✓

The columns (A–O) correspond to the Primary National Strategy objectives listed in the legend below the table.

Topic	A	B	C	D	E	F	G	H	I	J	K	L	M	N	O
Place value															
Fractions		✓													
Decimals	✓								✓						
Percentages		✓													
Addition	✓		✓												
Subtraction	✓		✓												
Money	✓		✓												
Time	✓														
Measures	✓								✓						
Puzzles															
Patterns and sequences	✓														
Multiplication	✓		✓						✓						
Division	✓		✓												
2D shapes					✓										
3D shapes				✓	✓										
Position and direction						✓	✓								
Data handling													✓	✓	
Two-step problems	✓	✓													

Legend — Primary National Strategy objectives

A. **Use efficient written methods to add and subtract integers and decimals, to multiply and divide integers and decimals by a one-digit integer, and to multiply two-digit and three-digit integers by a two-digit integer**

B. Relate fractions to multiplication and division (e.g. $6 \div 2 = \frac{1}{2}$ of $6 = 6 \times \frac{1}{2}$); express a quotient as a fraction or decimal (e.g. $67 \div 5 = 13.4$ or $13\frac{2}{5}$); find fractions and percentages of whole-number quantities (e.g. $\frac{5}{8}$ of 96, 65% of £260)

C. Use a calculator to solve problems involving multi-step calculations

Understanding shape

D. Describe, identify and visualise parallel and perpendicular edges or faces; use these properties to classify 2-D shapes and 3-D solids

E. Make and draw shapes with increasing accuracy and apply knowledge of their properties

F. **Visualise and draw on grids of different types where a shape will be after reflection, after translations, or after rotation through 90° or 180° about its centre or one of its vertices**

G. Use coordinates in the first quadrant to draw, locate and complete shapes that meet given properties

H. Estimate angles, and use a protractor to measure and draw them, on their own and in shapes; calculate angles in a triangle or around a point

Measuring

I. **Select and use standard metric units of measure and convert between units using decimals to two places (e.g. change 2.75 litres to 2750 ml, or vice versa)**

J. Read and interpret scales on a range of measuring instruments, recognising that the measurement made is approximate and recording results to a required degree of accuracy; compare readings on different scales, for example when using different instruments

K. Calculate the perimeter and area of rectilinear shapes; estimate the area of an irregular shape by counting squares

Handling data

L. Describe and predict outcomes from data using the language of chance or likelihood

M. **Solve problems by collecting, selecting, processing, presenting and interpreting data, using ICT where appropriate; draw conclusions and identify further questions to ask**

N. Construct and interpret frequency tables, bar charts with grouped discrete data, and line graphs; interpret pie charts

O. Describe and interpret results and solutions to problems using the mode, range, median and mean

How to use this book

This book is designed to help you use your mathematical skills to solve a range a problems, many of which are written in words rather than figures.

Rather than giving a calculation like:

$4 \times 6 = $ ☐

a word problem might be along the lines of:

"If I have 4 six-packs of cola, how many cans of cola do I have in total?"

The answer is the same, but you need to think about it a bit more and remember to answer by writing or saying: "I have 24 cans of cola in total."

The introduction

This section of each page gives you an idea of the sort of problems you are likely to see and helps you to understand what maths you need to use.

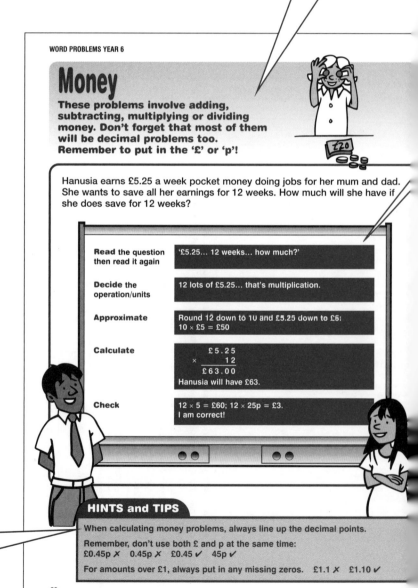

WORD PROBLEMS YEAR 6

Money

These problems involve adding, subtracting, multiplying or dividing money. Don't forget that most of them will be decimal problems too. Remember to put in the '£' or 'p'!

Hanusia earns £5.25 a week pocket money doing jobs for her mum and dad. She wants to save all her earnings for 12 weeks. How much will she have if she does save for 12 weeks?

Read the question then read it again	'£5.25... 12 weeks... how much?'
Decide the operation/units	12 lots of £5.25... that's multiplication.
Approximate	Round 12 down to 10 and £5.25 down to £5: 10 × £5 = £50
Calculate	£5.25 × 12 £63.00 Hanusia will have £63.
Check	12 × 5 = £60; 12 × 25p = £3. I am correct!

HINTS and TIPS

When calculating money problems, always line up the decimal points.

Remember, don't use both £ and p at the same time:
£0.45p ✗   0.45p ✗   £0.45 ✓   45p ✓

For amounts over £1, always put in any missing zeros.   £1.1 ✗   £1.10 ✓

22

Hints and tips

The hints and tips section gives you useful ideas for completing the problems on the other page. These are the things you need to remember if you are doing a quiz or test!

The example problem

The flow chart takes you through an example problem *step-by-step*. This is important when answering word problems as it helps you to order your thoughts, do each part of the problem in the right order and *check your work*!

Every problem has the same five steps.
READ the question then read it again
DECIDE your operations and units
APPROXIMATE your answer
CALCULATE
CHECK your answer

We remember this by using this mnemonic:

RAIN
DROPS
ARE
CRYSTAL
CLEAR

MONEY

Questions

(a) Hanusia decides to spend £2.50 a week and save £2.75. How much has she saved after 25 weeks?

(b) Hanusia's dad, Wasim, wants to buy a new garden shed. He saves £35 a week. For how many weeks will he have to save if the shed costs £525?

(c) Hanusia's mum, Januja, has saved £110. She offers to put it towards the shed costing £525. How much more would be needed to pay for the shed?

(a) Hanusia wants to buy some tools for her dad's shed. There is a sale on at the DIY shop. Each tool costs £6.99. Hanusia has £40. What is the largest number of tools she can buy? How much change will she get?

(b) Januja wants to buy some packets of seeds. She buys six packets of seeds each costing £2.95 and a garden hose to water the seeds for £25. How much does she spend altogether?

Challenge

Hanusia and her family are going to live in Italy where the currency is the euro. There are 1.6 euros to the pound. Hanusia's parents sell their house for £129,500.

How many euros can they spend on a new house in Italy?

Use a written method or a calculator.

23

The questions

The questions get harder as you go down the page.

● Section 1 questions are fairly straightforward and help you to practise your skills.
● Section 2 questions are a bit harder but will help you to remember all the key points.
● The Challenge sections are really tough and sometimes mean that you can make up games and your own questions! They can be great fun!

All about word problems

Ten top tips for working with word problems

1 *Work step-by-step.* Follow the flow chart.

RAIN	**R**ead the question then read it again
DROPS	**D**ecide your operations and units
ARE	**A**pproximate your answer
CRYSTAL	**C**alculate
CLEAR	**C**heck your answer

2 Always *show your working* or 'method'. This will help you to keep track of what you have done and may help you to get extra marks.

3 Always *include your units* in the answer. If you don't, you won't get full marks.

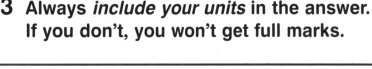

4 When you first read through a question, *underline important words and numbers*. This will help you to remember the important bits!

5 *Draw a picture to help you.* Sometimes a question is easier if you can 'see' it. Drawing 6 apples can help you if you need to divide them!

6 If the problem has a number of steps, break it down and do *one step at a time*.

7 When you *check your answers*, look at the inverse operation.

8 Sometimes an answer will 'sound right'. Read it out (quietly) and listen. *Does it make sense?*

9 If you are using measurements (grams, litres, cm), make sure that the *units are the same* before you calculate.

10 Once again! *Read the question and check that your solution answers it.*

Place value

Place value questions often ask you to make up a large or small number using different digits. Remember, each digit has a different value depending on where you put it.

Amar has five digit cards: 6, 3, 8, 9 and 4. He can only use each card once. What is the largest 4-digit number he can make? Write your answer in words.

Read the question then read it again	'Write your answer in words...'
Decide the operation/units	I'm ordering the digits. Largest one first.
Approximate	The number will be nine thousand and something.
Calculate	9 then 8 then 6 then 4. The largest 4-digit number Amar can make is nine thousand, eight hundred and sixty-four.
Check	Yes, the number is the largest and it's spelt correctly.

HINTS and TIPS

Multiplying by a thousand is the same as multiplying by 10, then by 10 again and by 10 again.

For example:
1000 × 2 is the same as calculating: 2 × 10 = 20; 20 × 10 = 200; 200 × 10 = 2000

Questions

1

(a) What is the smallest 4-digit odd number Amar can make with his cards? Write your answer in words.

(b) What is the second largest 4-digit number Amar can make with his cards? Write your answer in words.

(c) What is the second smallest 4-digit number Amar can make with his cards? Write your answer in words.

2

(a) Amar swaps all five of his cards for five *different* digit cards. What is the largest 4-digit number he can make if he only uses each new card once? Write your answer in words.

(b) What is the smallest 4-digit number Amar can make with his cards if he is allowed to use any three odd digits and one even digit?

Challenge

Place the digits 9, 4, 7, 6, 5, 1 in the boxes in order to get the largest result.

(☐☐ × ☐☐ + ☐) × ☐ = ☐☐☐☐

Fractions

Fraction problems are tricky. You might be asked to find a fraction of a number, e.g. 'What is half of 30?' You may also be asked to work out 'What fraction of 30 is 15?'

George spends 39 weeks of the year at work as a teacher and 13 weeks of the year on holiday. What fraction of the year does George spend on holiday?

Read the question then read it again	'What fraction... on holiday...'
Decide the operation/units	13 weeks *out of* 52... that's division!
Approximate	52 weeks in a year... a quarter?
Calculate	$\frac{13}{52} = \frac{1}{4}$ George spends $\frac{1}{4}$ of the year on holiday.
Check	Yes, $\frac{1}{4}$ of 52 is 13, which is the same as dividing 52 by 4... which is 13. I was correct!

HINTS and TIPS

Finding $\frac{1}{2}$ of something is the same as dividing it by 2; finding $\frac{1}{3}$ of something is the same as dividing it by 3; finding $\frac{1}{4}$ of something is the same as dividing it by 4... etc.

If you want to find $\frac{2}{3}$ of something, find $\frac{1}{3}$ first, then multiply by 2.
To find $\frac{3}{4}$ of something, find one quarter first, then multiply by 3 etc.

Questions

APRIL 8TH

1

(a) George spends 39 weeks a year at work as a teacher. What fraction of the year is this?

(b) Georgina is a part-time teacher. She works for 26 weeks a year as a supply teacher. For what fraction of the year does Georgina work?

(c) What fraction of the year does George spend on holiday abroad if his family go abroad for 2 two-week holidays a year?

2

(a) George spends $\frac{3}{10}$ of his 40-day summer holiday preparing lessons and marking books. How many days is this?

(b) Georgina travels around the world from August 1st to 31st December. What fraction of the year is this in months?

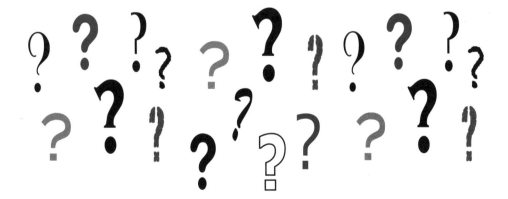

Challenge

If George spends $\frac{2}{3}$ of his 39 weeks at work in the classroom and Georgina spends $\frac{11}{13}$ of her 26 weeks at work in the classroom, who spends the most time in class and by how much?

Decimals

Decimal problems can be about distance or time. Don't forget to write in the units! These questions use addition and subtraction but watch out for the Challenge!

At the school sports day, Kamilah came second in the long jump with a leap of 2.7 m. Lauren jumped 350 mm further and won. How far in metres did Lauren jump?

Read the question then read it again	'2.7 m... 350 mm... how far?'
Decide the operation/units	Addition and metres.
Approximate	The answer will be more than 3 metres but it must be realistic.
Calculate	2.7 m = 270 cm 350 mm = 35 cm 270 cm + 35 cm = 305 cm Lauren jumped 3.05 m.
Check	305 cm – 35 cm = 270 cm. I'm correct.

HINTS and TIPS

When dealing with mixed decimals such as 2.3 and 1.74, add any missing zeros to make ordering or calculating much easier.

For example: 2.3 + 1.74 becomes *2.30* + 1.74

Questions

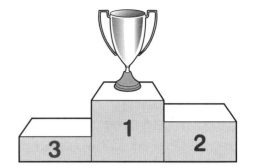

1

(a) Kamilah threw the discus 11.8 m.
This was 600 mm further than Lauren.
How far in metres did Lauren throw
the discus?

(b) Lauren ran the 200 m sprint in 30.9 seconds. Kamilah was 1.2 seconds
faster. What was Kamilah's time for the 200 m?

(c) Kamilah cleared 1.61 m in the high jump. Marie jumped 150 mm less.
How high in metres did Marie jump?

2

(a) Grant, Oprah and Lisa played in a basketball tournament. Grant took
28.12 seconds to shoot 8 baskets. Lisa was 3.58 seconds quicker than
Grant but 2.35 seconds slower than Oprah. What was Oprah's time
in seconds?

(b) Grant, Oprah and Lisa also ran in the school cross country race.
This time Grant was 240 seconds faster than Oprah who finished in
25.5 minutes. Lisa was 600 seconds slower than Oprah. How much
faster was Grant than Lisa?

Challenge

All five children formed a tug of war team.
This is how much each of them weighed.

Grant 46.83 kg, Lisa 35.27 kg, Lauren 41.59 kg,
Marie 44.42 kg, Oprah 46.80 kg

They won three matches in a row before losing in the
final to a team that was 5500 g lighter than them.
How heavy was the winning team? Give your answer in kg.

Percentages

Percentage problems are often about money. Some questions ask for a percentage of an amount of money, e.g. 10% of £1. Other questions might ask you to work out 10% off a price.

Jordan wants to buy a new pair of trainers. A pair of 'Reeburks' are priced at £35 but are on special offer with 20% off the price. How much would Jordan pay for the trainers now?

Read the question then read it again	'£35... 20% off... how much?'
Decide the operation/units	Percent means 'out of a hundred'. The units are £.
Approximate	20% is the same as a fifth...
Calculate	10% of 35 = 3.5 so 20% = 7. £35 – £7 = £28 Jordan would pay £28 for the trainers.
Check	28 + 7 = 35

HINTS and TIPS

Learn these percentage/decimal/fraction equivalents (equivalent means 'the same').

$1\% = 0.01 = \frac{1}{100}$ $25\% = 0.25 = \frac{1}{4}$

$10\% = 0.1 = \frac{1}{10}$ $50\% = 0.5 = \frac{1}{2}$

$20\% = 0.2 = \frac{1}{5}$ $75\% = 0.75 = \frac{3}{4}$

You can find percentages by halving and quartering.

For example,
12.5% of £48,000
50% = £24,000
25% = £12,000
12.5% = £6000

Questions

1

(a) Jordan's dad Steve goes to the sports shop. He sees a pair of socks at £3. At the till he is offered a 30% discount because it is an end of season sale. How much would Steve pay?

(b) Jordan's sister Stacey wants to have tennis lessons. The normal price is £20 per hour but during Wimbledon there is an amazing 60% off! How much is a tennis lesson during Wimbledon?

(c) Jordan joins the local athletics club. The cost of membership is £300 per year with 70% off for under 16s. Jordan is 11. How much does he pay to join for a year?

2

(a) Stacey is trying to choose a new coat for Christmas. She sees the same coat in two places. At the supermarket the coat is £70 with a 30% discount. In the department store the coat is £50. Which one should she buy? What is the difference in price?

(b) Steve's golf lessons have gone up! They used to cost £12 per lesson but are up by 20%. How much does Steve pay for a golf lesson now?

Challenge

Steve, Jordan and Stacey each have £1300 saved in the bank. Steve takes out 70%, Jordan takes 10% and Stacey takes 15% to spend on holiday. They each come home with 10% of their spending money left. How much does each of them have when they get home?

Addition

Most of these addition problems ask you to add two 4-digit numbers. That can be tricky. Remember to line up the numbers accurately in the sum – then you will be fine.

Charlie and Tony collect crisp packet labels for their school. Charlie has 5834 and Tony has 2183. How many do they have altogether?

Read the question then read it again	'5834... 2183... altogether...'
Decide the operation/units	'Altogether' means add.
Approximate	5834 is close to 5800, 2183 is close to 2200. 5800 + 2200 = 8000
Calculate	$$\begin{array}{r} 5\ 8\ 3\ 4 \\ +\ 2\ 1\ 8\ 3 \\ \hline 8\ 0\ 1\ 7 \end{array}$$ Charlie and Tony have 8017 crisp packet labels.
Check	I'll check using the inverse method. 8017 – 5834 = 2183 Also, 8017 is very close to my estimate.

HINTS and TIPS

'increase by'   'how many altogether'   'add'

'what is the total of...'   'find the sum of...'

All these terms and phrases mean ADDITION.

Questions

1

(a) Josh has 2472 crisp packet labels and Luke gives him 989 that his Gran had saved for them. How many labels does Josh have in total?

(b) Luke has 1760 crisp packet labels. He increases his collection by 1348. How many labels does he have now?

(c) Amy and Ivy start collecting. Amy has 1549 crisp packet labels and Ivy has 1468. What is the sum of Amy and Ivy's collection?

2

(a) To complete the collection and qualify for a free tennis ball for your school, you need to have 10 000 labels. Charlie has now got 9341 and Tony has 3895. How many labels more than 10 000 do they have between them?

(b) Amy has 1549 crisp packet labels but Ivy gets bored with collecting and gives her 1468 labels to Amy. Charlie and Tony have got their tennis ball so they give all their spares [see question 2(a)] to Amy. How many labels does Amy have now? Does she qualify for a tennis ball?

Challenge

Josh sets Luke a challenge. Josh shows Luke a grid of 16 squares.

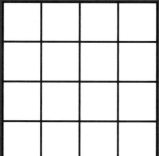

Luke must place a crisp packet label on the first square then double the number of labels on each square until he has filled the grid. How many labels would there be on the sixteenth square? How many tennis balls could he get? [see question 2(a)]

What if the grid was 5 × 5? How many labels would there be on the twenty-fifth square?

How many tennis balls would he get now? You may need extra paper for this one.

Subtraction

Most of these subtraction problems are taking away a 4-digit number from another 4-digit number. Estimating first will help you get these right.

Rochelle and Mary played pinball in the amusement arcade by the seaside. Rochelle scored 5395 points and Mary scored 3228 less than Rochelle. How many points did Mary score?

Read the question then read it again	'5395... 3228... less than...'
Decide the operation/units	'Less than' means subtract.
Approximate	Rounding method... 5400 – 3200 = 2200
Calculate	$$\begin{array}{r} 5\ 3\ 9\ 5 \\ -\ 3\ 2\ 2\ 8 \\ \hline 2\ 1\ 6\ 7 \end{array}$$ Mary scored 2167 points.
Check	2167 + 3228 = 5395 Also, 2167 is close to my estimate.

HINTS and TIPS

'less than'   'difference'   'decrease'   'subtract'
All these terms and phrases mean SUBTRACTION.

When subtracting 4-digit numbers, make sure you line up the digits in the calculation carefully.

Always check your answer by using addition.

Questions

1

(a) Ivan and Billy played a game of pinball. Billy scored 6467 fewer points than Ivan who scored 8821. How many points did Billy score?

(b) Billy got his own back on the 'Virtual Space Ranger' game! He scored 8462 points and Ivan scored 2836 less. How many did Ivan score?

(c) Rochelle and Mary tried the same game. Mary scored 949 and Rochelle scored 9588. What was the difference between the two scores?

2

(a) Mary bought herself, Joe, Hannah and Jonathan 'kiss me quick' hats costing £2.70 each. How much change did she get from a £20 note?

(b) Rochelle, Mary, Ivan and Billy had a game of 'Tecken 4'. The girls scored 8725 points. The boys scored 1753 less. Ivan scored 4281 points. How many did Billy score?

Challenge

Here are some famous dates in history.

1963 – President Kennedy assassinated
1909 – First flight across the English Channel
1815 – Wellington defeats Napoleon at Waterloo
1666 – The Great Fire of London
1564 – The birth of Shakespeare
3500 BC – Stonehenge is built

Write down the current year (2007, 2008 etc).

Can you work out how many years ago these events took place?

Money

These problems involve adding, subtracting, multiplying or dividing money. Don't forget that most of them will be decimal problems too. Remember to put in the '£' or 'p'!

Hanusia earns £5.25 a week pocket money doing jobs for her mum and dad. She wants to save all her earnings for 12 weeks. How much will she have if she does save for 12 weeks?

Read the question then read it again	'£5.25... 12 weeks... how much?'
Decide the operation/units	12 lots of £5.25... that's multiplication.
Approximate	Round 12 down to 10 and £5.25 down to £5: 10 × £5 = £50
Calculate	£ 5.25 × 12 ———— £ 6 3.00 Hanusia will have £63.
Check	12 × 5 = £60; 12 × 25p = £3. I am correct!

HINTS and TIPS

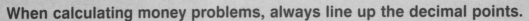

When calculating money problems, always line up the decimal points.

Remember, don't use both £ and p at the same time:
£0.45p ✗   0.45p ✗   £0.45 ✔   45p ✔

For amounts over £1, always put in any missing zeros.   £1.1 ✗   £1.10 ✔

Questions

1

(a) Hanusia decides to spend £2.50 a week and save £2.75.
How much has she saved after 25 weeks?

(b) Hanusia's dad, Wasim, wants to buy a new garden shed.
He saves £35 a week. For how many weeks will he have to save
if the shed costs £525?

(c) Hanusia's mum, Januja, has saved £110. She offers to put it towards
the shed costing £525. How much more would be needed to pay for
the shed?

2

(a) Hanusia wants to buy some tools for her dad's shed. There is a sale
on at the DIY shop. Each tool costs £6.99. Hanusia has £40. What is the
largest number of tools she can buy? How much change will she get?

(b) Januja wants to buy some packets of seeds.
She buys six packets of seeds each costing £2.95
and a garden hose to water the seeds for £25.
How much does she spend altogether?

Challenge

Hanusia and her family are going to live in Italy where
the currency is the euro. There are 1.6 euros to the pound.
Hanusia's parents sell their house for £129,500.

How many euros can they spend on
a new house in Italy?

Use a written method or a calculator.

Time

Time problems often ask you to work out how many minutes there are between two times. They may also ask you to work out what time is 30 minutes later than, say, 13:00. Remember the 24 hour clock!

Kieron and his friends are visiting 'Chunder Towers' amusement park for a birthday treat. They arrive at 09:43 and stay until 16:52. How long do they stay at the park?

Read the question then read it again	'09:43... 16:52... how long?'
Decide the operation/units	Counting on. It's addition... hours and minutes.
Approximate	9 count on to 16 = 7 hours
Calculate	09:43 + 7 hours = 16:43 16:43 + 9 minutes = 16:52 They stay for 7 hours and 9 minutes.
Check	My answer is close to my estimate of 7 hours.

HINTS and TIPS

1 millennium = 1000 years
1 century = 100 years
1 decade = 10 years
1 year = 12 months or 52 weeks or 365 days
1 leap year = 366 days ('Olympic years' are
leap years: 2004, 2000, 1996, 1992 etc.)

1 week = 7 days
1 day = 24 hours
1 hour = 60 minutes
1 minute = 60 seconds

Questions

1 (a) Kieron wants to go on the 'Water Chute'. He begins queuing at 10:45 and gets on the ride at 11:02. How long does he have to queue?

(b) Kieron, Adam and Ronnie all want to have a go at panning for gold in 'Thunder River'. They start panning at 11:27 and finish at 12:10. How long do they pan for gold?

(c) The boat trip starts at 12:10 and lasts for 55 minutes. At what time do Kieron, Ronnie and Adam finish the trip?

2 (a) Kieron and his friends have lunch at 13:15. They have to wait 9 minutes for their hotdogs to cook, queue for 14 minutes at a stall for some drinks and spend 23 minutes eating and drinking. At what time do they finish eating and drinking?

(b) At 14:05 the 'Wild Frontier Rodeo Show' begins! The show is made up of a 16 minute sing-along, 19 minutes of lasso tricks, 25 minutes of horse-riding stunts and 11 minutes of cowboys on 'bucking broncos'. At what time does the show end?

Challenge

Kieron's, Ronnie's and Adam's birthdays are on January 5th, March 14th and May 12th.
Can you work out how many days it is to their birthdays from today's date?

How many days is it until your birthday?

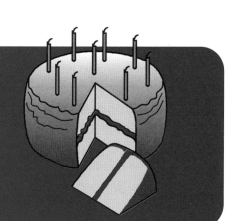

Measures

Measures questions can be about weight, capacity or length. Add, subtract, multiply or divide to get the answers. Remember to put in the units!

Triptonfell Rugby club has a pot containing 325 litres of spicy parsnip soup for the spectators. One cup of soup is 200 ml. How many spectators can have a cup of spicy parsnip soup?

Read the question then read it again	'325 litres... 200 ml...'
Decide the operation/units	How many *lots of* 200 ml in 325 litres?
Approximate	How many 200 ml in *1 litre* first of all?
Calculate	1 litre = 1000 ml. 1000 ml ÷ 200 ml = 5 so 325 × 5 = 1625. 1625 spectators can have a cup of soup.
Check	1625 × 200 ml = 325 000 ml = 325 litres

HINTS and TIPS

When calculating kg and g or l and ml, first convert the units so they are the same.

e.g. 2 kg + 500 g
     converts to
     2000 g + 500 g

'Milli' means a thousand in Latin.
1000 years in a millennium, 1000 mm in a metre.

'Kilo' means a thousand in Greek.
1000 g in a kilogram, 1000 m in a kilometre.

'Centi' means a hundred in Latin.
100 cm in a metre, 100 cl in a litre,
100 years in a century.

Questions

1

(a) The rugby pitch is 75.5 m long. The groundsman lengthens it by 575 cm. How long is the pitch now in metres?

(b) Brendan's kicking boot weighs 400 g. If all the team's boots each weigh the same, how much do 12 kicking boots weigh?

(c) Brendan can kick a rugby ball 28 m. Brendan's coach can kick a ball $2\frac{1}{4}$ times further. How far can the coach kick the ball?

2

(a) Brendan passes the ball to Stephen and it travels 5.84 m. He kicks the ball a further 24.65 m up the pitch. How many centimetres has the ball travelled?

(b) Triptonfell Rugby club orders 5000 litres of shandy. It sells an average of 125 litres per day. How long does its supply of shandy last?

Challenge

Two teams of 15 hungry players eat sandwiches and cakes after the match. Each player eats 450 g of sandwiches and 375 g of cakes.

How many kilograms of food are eaten by the teams?

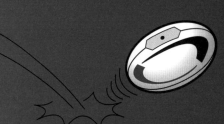

Puzzles

Number puzzles are great fun but you have to think step-by-step to get them right! It can really help to underline key words in these questions.

Who am I? I have three digits and I am less than 130.
I can be divided exactly by 3 and 8.

Read the question then read it again	I need to work methodically...
Decide the operation/units	Dividing 3-digit numbers by 3 and 8.
Approximate	As it can be divided by 8 and is under 130 it must be... 104, 112, 120 or 128
Calculate	The only number out of those that can be divided by 3 is 120. I am 120!
Check	Double-check my answer... I am correct.

HINTS and TIPS

When you solve puzzles it helps to work 'methodically'. This means taking things step-by-step. Test your ideas.

Sometimes drawing pictures can help you to solve the problems.

Questions

1

(a) Who am I? I am a 2-digit number.
The sum of my digits is 6.
My units digit is two times my tens digit.

(b) Fatma is thinking of a 3-digit odd number.
The hundreds digit is three times more than
the units digit. The sum of the three digits is 4.
What number is Fatma thinking off?

(c) Rachel opened her Maths book and found that
the sum of the facing page numbers was 245.
What pages did she open the Maths book to?

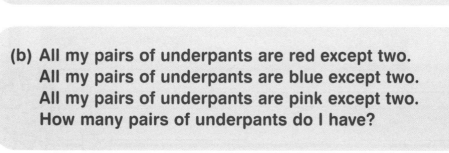

2

(a) The ages of Alan and Martin add up to 99.
Alan's age is Martin's age reversed.
How old are Alan and Martin?

(b) All my pairs of underpants are red except two.
All my pairs of underpants are blue except two.
All my pairs of underpants are pink except two.
How many pairs of underpants do I have?

Challenge

Who am I?

I have three digits.
I can only be divided by myself and one.
The sum of my digits is 11.
I am greater than 120 but less than 150.

Patterns and sequences

Pattern questions might ask you to find the 'nth' number in a pattern or to work out how many numbers are in the pattern. These questions are all about comets.

Halley's Comet last crossed our skies in 1986. The time before that was 1910 and the time before that was 1834. When do you think Halley's Comet will appear again?

Read the question then read it again	'Comets?'
Decide the operation/units	I'm looking for the *difference between* the years.
Approximate	The year 2050?
Calculate	The difference between the years is 76 each time. 1986 + 76 = 2062 I think Halley's Comet will reappear in 2062.
Check	Yes, those years fit the sequence of the comet appearing every 76 years.

HINTS and TIPS

When asked to predict the next number in a sequence, start looking at the rest of the numbers and how they relate to each other. Work out their differences.

Questions

1

(a) Halley's Comet appears every 76 years. The next appearance of Halley's Comet will be in 2062. When will the next three appearances be after that?

(b) Halley's Comet appeared before the battle of Hastings in 1066. When were its next three appearances?

(c) When were its previous three appearances before 1066?

2

(a) How many appearances from Halley's Comet can we expect in the next 500 years?

(b) The comet Denning-Fujikawa was discovered in 1879. It can be seen every 9 years. How many times has it been seen since its discovery and this current year?

Challenge

Comets are named after the people who first discover them.

Write down a two-digit number. This is how often your 'comet' appears. Ask a friend to give you a date from any time in the last 1000 years. Calculate how many times your 'comet' has been sighted since that date. Try with 3-digit numbers and longer passages of time.

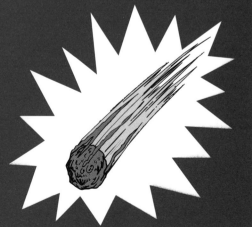

Multiplication

Multiplication problems are story problems. They are often about measures or money. The key is to work out what numbers you are multiplying and add the units!

Bella has 24 apple trees on her farm. She picks 168 from each one to make some apple pies. How many apples has she picked?

Read the question then read it again	'24 trees... 168 from each...'
Decide the operation/units	24 *lots of* 168... multiplication
Approximate	Round 24 down to 20... $20 \times 170 = 3400$
Calculate	$\begin{array}{r} 1\,6\,8 \\ \times\quad 2\,4 \\ \hline 4\,0\,3\,2 \end{array}$ Bella has picked 4032 apples.
Check	4032 is fairly close to my estimate. Also, $4032 \div 24 = 168$.

HINTS and TIPS

'times' 'multiply' 'multiplied by' 'lots of' 'product'

All these words and phrases mean MULTIPLICATION. Learn them.

If you are asked to 'find the product of these two numbers' make sure you multiply them – don't add them!

Questions

1

(a) Bella sells 382 apple pies for 65p each. How much in total does she sell all the pies for?

(b) Bella has 52 boxes of cherries each containing 250 g of cherries. How many kilograms of cherries does she have?

(c) Bella sells the boxes of cherries for 75p a box. How much does she get for selling all 52 boxes?

2

(a) Bella's farm is doing well. Bella makes £630 for 30 weeks of the year and £450 a week for 22 weeks of the year. How much does Bella make over the course of the year?

(b) The farm starts selling different sorts of fruit pies. Bella sells 624 cherry pies, 472 plum pies and 283 apple and raspberry pies. The pies are now sold at 95p each, but they each cost Bella 27p to make. How much profit does Bella make when she sells all the pies?

Challenge

Bella starts a 'pick-your-own' business on her fruit farm. She charges £2.99 per kilogram of strawberries picked.

Max picks 18 kg and Judy picks 42 kg! How much do Max and Judy have to pay altogether?

Discuss your method of calculation with a partner.

Division

These division problems are all about a brand new band! Work out which number to divide (the bigger one usually). Don't forget to put in the units! Watch out! There are some big numbers here!

The latest boy band, 'Boyz-U-Really-Prefer' or 'B.U.R.P.', are holding a concert. Their fan club of 432 screaming girls are packed equally onto 24 mini-buses to get there. How many girls are there on each mini-bus?

Read the question then read it again	'432... 24 mini-buses... how many girls on each?'
Decide the operation/units	24 *into* 432. That's division.
Approximate	20 into 400 = 20
Calculate	$$\begin{array}{r} 1\ 8 \\ 24\overline{)4\ 3\ 2} \\ 2\ 4\ 0 \quad (24 \times 10) \\ \overline{1\ 9\ 2} \\ 1\ 9\ 2 \quad (24 \times 8) \\ \overline{0} \end{array}$$ There are 18 girls on each mini-bus.
Check	My estimate was close. I'll check using the inverse method. 18 × 24 = 432. I was correct!

HINTS and TIPS

Remember, multiplication is the opposite of division.
Use it to check your answers.

Questions

1

(a) B.U.R.P. are playing at Wembley Arena, which holds 5000 people. How many coach-loads of 50 fans can fit inside?

(b) Twelve fans pay a total of £960 for front row seats and backstage passes. How much do they pay equally between them?

(c) Sixteen fans paid a total of £720 for autographed hankies used by the band! How much did each fan pay equally for an autographed hankie?

2

(a) B.U.R.P. went on tour. They played 25 songs at every concert. Each concert lasted $2\frac{1}{2}$ hours. How many minutes did each song last on average?

(b) B.U.R.P. eventually became unfashionable and ended up playing at children's birthday parties. They charged £87.50 for an afternoon's performance. There were seven members of the band. They split the money equally. How much did each of them get for a children's party?

Challenge

Use a calculator for this one.

At the height of their fame, B.U.R.P. made £1,000,000! However... this was divided between the seven members of the band. Each member's share was then taxed at 50%. Each member then had to pay 50% of what was left to their agent and then 50% of what was left again to the record company. Another 50% was deducted to cover expenses.

How much did each member end up with?

2D shapes

These questions are about the properties of 2D shapes. If it helps you can draw each of the questions step-by-step.

Raymond has a number of regular polygons (shapes with straight sides that are the same length as each other). He experiments by sliding shapes together to make new ones. He always lines up the sides so that they meet exactly.

Raymond slides an equilateral triangle next to a square to form a new shape. What is the name of the new shape?

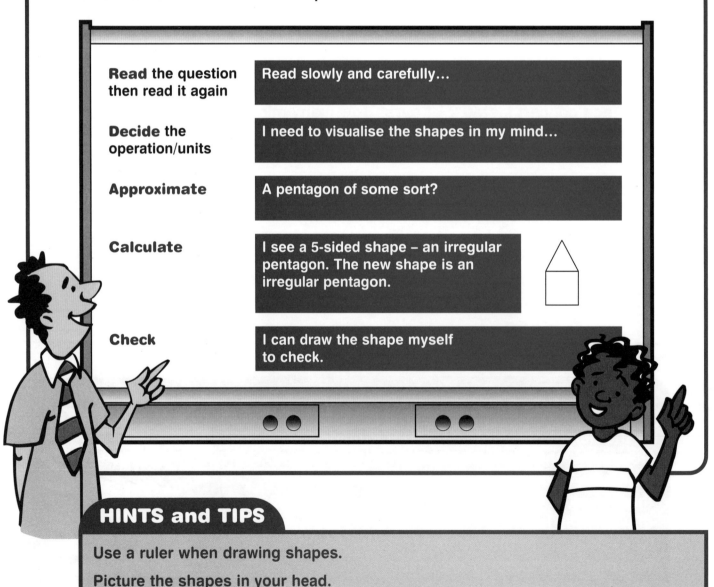

Read the question then read it again	Read slowly and carefully...
Decide the operation/units	I need to visualise the shapes in my mind...
Approximate	A pentagon of some sort?
Calculate	I see a 5-sided shape – an irregular pentagon. The new shape is an irregular pentagon.
Check	I can draw the shape myself to check.

HINTS and TIPS

Use a ruler when drawing shapes.

Picture the shapes in your head.

Remember the language.

Questions

1

(a) Raymond puts two equilateral triangles together.
How many sides does the new shape have?

(b) Amber has a go. She puts three equilateral triangles together.
What is the name of this new shape?

(c) Amber and Raymond take one more equilateral triangle and add it to Amber's shape. What three shapes can they make? How many sides does each have?

2

(a) Raymond starts using more shapes. He takes a hexagon and places an equilateral triangle flush on each of the hexagon's sides. How many sides does this new shape have?

(b) Amber makes a shape that looks like a sunflower! She takes an octagon and slides a square onto each of the octagon's sides. How many sides does the 'sunflower shape' have?

Challenge

Set yourself a time limit to unscramble these shape related words. Under five minutes – you're in great shape!

circle
diagonal
equilateral
heptagon
hexagon
isosceles
kite
octagon

parallelogram
pentagon
polygon
quadrilateral
rectangle
square
trapezium
triangle

x	h	e	p	t	a	g	o	n	l	a	w	e	r	y
p	f	b	a	d	p	e	n	t	a	g	o	n	p	u
y	g	h	p	a	z	q	d	i	a	g	o	n	a	l
i	k	s	d	r	b	u	j	s	z	m	c	e	r	r
s	e	c	j	k	c	i	r	c	l	e	t	q	a	h
q	u	a	d	r	i	l	a	t	e	r	a	l	l	o
u	i	l	e	a	q	a	t	r	a	d	g	p	l	m
a	v	e	t	u	o	t	k	i	t	e	o	o	e	b
r	u	n	g	r	h	e	x	a	g	o	n	l	l	u
e	q	e	g	d	z	r	u	n	o	h	l	y	o	s
s	o	r	e	c	t	a	n	g	l	e	c	g	g	c
t	p	a	r	a	l	l	e	l	e	f	s	o	r	l
b	m	u	i	s	o	s	c	e	l	e	s	n	a	j
f	a	b	u	t	r	a	p	e	z	i	u	m	m	h

3D shapes

3D shape questions will often ask you to recognise shapes and describe their properties. You will be expected to visualise the movement of shapes or recognise their nets.

Karen is looking at the net of a cube. The base is shaded. She has to find the square which will be the top of the cube.

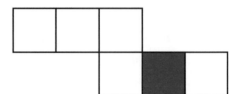

Read the question then read it again	Read slowly and carefully…
Decide the operation/units	I'm looking for a 3D shape…
Approximate	It will be a face that is not touching the base…
Calculate	It will be this face… 
Check	Cut it out and fold it up.

HINTS and TIPS

3D shapes have 'faces' (the flat parts) 'edges' (the long sharp parts) and vertices (the short sharp parts where the edges meet).

Questions

1

Here are the nets of three cubes.

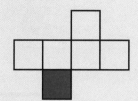 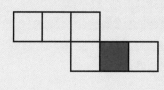 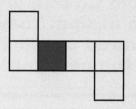

The shaded square in each case is the base of the cube. The top is white. Your task is to draw arrows on the other four faces so that when the net is folded into a cube and you look at any face, the arrow points to your right.

Here is an example of a net with arrows drawn on its faces and folded into a cube:

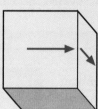

2

Sort these shapes into the correct places on the Carroll diagram.

cube, tetrahedron, cylinder, square-based pyramid

	At least one pair of parallel faces	No parallel faces
At least one pair of perpendicular edges		
No perpendicular edges		

Challenge

Complete this table and then see if you can spot a connection between the number of faces, edges and vertices for each shape.

	Number of faces	Number of vertices	Number of edges
Tetrahedron			
Cube			
Square-based pyramid			
Triangular prism			
Octahedron			

Position and direction

Alan and Charlie are planning a new garden design. They complete their design on squared paper. These questions are all about the new garden design.

Use the garden plan on page 41 to answer these questions.

The points (–3, 6), (–3, 3) and (3, 6) are three of the four vertices of the swimming pool. What are the coordinates of the fourth vertex?

Read the question then read it again	I need to work step-by-step.
Decide the operation/units	I'm working with coordinates...
Approximate	Remember, along then up or down.
Calculate	Find the coordinates already given. Identify the missing one on the grid. It is (3, 3). The coordinates of the fourth vertex of the swimming pool are (3, 3).
Check	Take the time to double-check.

HINTS and TIPS

Coordinates mark where the lines cross, not the spaces in between.

Remember, 'x' comes before 'y' in the alphabet. Always go ALONG the corridor then UP the stairs.

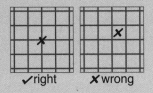

✓right ✗wrong

Questions

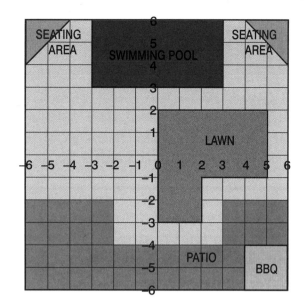

1

(a) What are the coordinates of the four vertices of the barbeque?

(b) If Alan was at the point (–2, 4) and Charlie was at the point (1, 5) what would they probably be doing?

(c) What are the coordinates of the two seating areas?

2

(a) Alan decides that the lawn needs developing. He wants it reflected symmetrically using the y axis as the mirror line. What would be the coordinates be of the four new vertices?

(b) Charlie decides to build a dining area in a position that reflects the barbeque using the y axis as the mirror line. What would the coordinates be of the four new vertices?

Challenge

Use squared paper. Draw x and y axes and use all four quadrants.
Design your own garden or playground. Plot the coordinates of the vertices of the main features and write three word problems for a friend to answer.

Data handling

Data handling questions will ask you to look at a chart, graph or table and use the data to answer the questions. Sometimes you will have to transfer data from a table to a chart.

A music magazine did a survey to find out the ages of fans who said that the ancient rock group 'Led Balloon' were their favourite band.

What is the most common age of the fans who said Led Balloon were their favourite band?

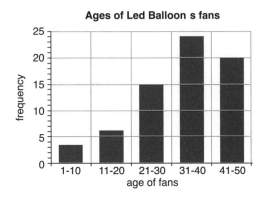

Read the question then read it again	I need to understand what the chart is telling me…
Decide the operation/units	The chart is telling me the frequency of the grouped ages of Led Balloon fans.
Approximate	I have to look at all the information that is given to me.
Calculate	The column showing the highest frequency is the fourth one, which is 31–40. The most common age for a Led Balloon fan is between 31 and 40.
Check	I can compare my answer with all the other possibilities – yes, I'm correct.

HINTS and TIPS

Always look at the titles of the graph and the axes first. They tell you what the information is about.

Questions

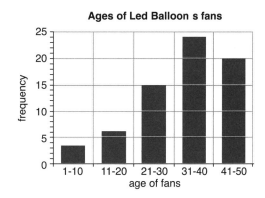

Ages of Led Balloon s fans

1

(a) Which age group of fans said Led Balloon were their favourite band the least number of times?

(b) Which age group appeared fifteen times in the survey?

(c) How many times did the 41–50 age group say that Led Balloon were their favourite band?

2

(a) How many people over 30 said Led Balloon were their favourite?

(b) How many Led Balloon fans did the magazine survey altogether?

Challenge

The magazine did another survey. This time they wanted to investigate the ages of fans who said that the teen idol 'Gareth Goats' (he's just a kid) was their favourite pop star.

Sketch a graph showing how you think the ages in the second survey would be shown.

Write three questions about your graph for a friend to answer.

Two·step problems

Two-step problems need you to think carefully and keep notes of each step. You will have to complete an operation, take the answer and do a further one or two operations to that answer to get the final answer.

Brights Park Primary are holding their Summer Fête. There are 67 stalls, 33 are selling things and half of the remainder are sideshow games. How many stalls are sideshow games?

Read the question then read it again	'67... 33... half of the remainder...'
Decide the operation/units	*Subtract* 33 from 67 then *divide* the answer by 2.
Approximate	$70 - 30 = 40$. $\frac{1}{2}$ of 40 = 20... 20 seems reasonable.
Calculate	$67 - 33 = 34$ *then* half of 34 = 17. 17 stalls are sideshow games.
Check	These are short calculations. I can redo them quickly to check.

HINTS and TIPS

Work out which part of a multi-step problem needs to be done first. Always show your working when writing down how you tackled a problem. Work methodically.

Questions

1

(a) Courtney and John are running the homemade cake stall.
Courtney sells £39 worth of cakes and John sells £45 worth.
They give £30 to the school and keep the rest for themselves.
How much money do Courtney and John keep?

(b) Cathy buys five strips of raffle tickets and Harrison buys four strips
of raffle tickets. The raffle tickets cost 75p a strip. How much do they
spend on raffle tickets altogether?

(c) Nicky and Tim are selling 'penny sweets'.
They started with 1600 sweets. Nicky sells 865
and Tim sells 667. How many sweets are left?
How much do they make in £ and pence?

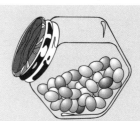

2

(a) Marlon and Ayden are running the 'throw wet sponges at the teacher'
stall. Marlon charges 35p per sponge and makes £19.60 and Ayden
charges 45p per sponge and makes £20.70. How many sponges were
thrown?

(b) Paul and Mel are running the lucky dip stall. By the end of the fete they
have made £157 for the school and £33 for themselves. However, before
they go home, Mel suggests they donate 15% of their total takings to
her favourite charity. Paul agrees. How much do they give to the
charity?

Challenge

Rose and Rene are running the 'hook a duck' stall. Rose asks Rene, 'If two
ducks are swimming in front of another duck, two ducks are swimming
behind another duck, and one duck is swimming between two other ducks,
what is the minimum number of ducks we can have?' Rene doesn't know!
Do you?

Answers

Place value

1 (a) Three thousand, four hundred and sixty-eight
(b) Nine thousand, eight hundred and sixty-three
(c) Three thousand, four hundred and sixty-nine

2 (a) Seven thousand, five hundred and twenty-one
(b) One thousand and fifty-seven

● Challenge
$(74 \times 65 + 1) \times 9 = 43\,299$

Fractions

1 (a) ¾   (b) ½   (c) ⅓

2 (a) 12 days
(b) ⁵⁄₁₂

● Challenge
George spends longer in the classroom by four weeks.

Decimals

1 (a) 11.2 m
(b) 29.7 seconds
(c) 1.46 m

2 (a) 22.19 seconds
(b) 14 minutes

● Challenge
209.41 kg

Percentages

1 (a) £2.10   (b) £8 an hour   (c) £90

2 (a) She should buy the coat from the supermarket because it's £1 cheaper.
(b) £14.40

● Challenge
Steve has £91, Jordan has £13 and Stacey has £19.50.

Addition

1 (a) 3461   (b) 3108   (c) 3017

2 (a) They have 3236 labels more than the 10,000 they need.
(b) Amy has 6253 labels so she doesn't qualify for a tennis ball!

● Challenge
First part: 32,768 labels and 3 tennis balls
Second part: 16,777,216 labels and 1,677 tennis balls

Subtraction

1 (a) 2354   (b) 5626   (c) 8639

2 (a) Mary got £9.20 change.
(b) Billy scored 2691

● Challenge
From 2007 the answers are:
44, 98, 192, 341, 443, 5507

Money

1 (a) She has saved £68.75
(b) 15 weeks
(c) £415

2 (a) Hanusia can buy 5 tools and keep £5.05 change.
(b) £42.70

● Challenge
They have 207,200 euros to spend.

Time

1 (a) Kieron queues for 17 minutes.
(b) 43 minutes
(c) 13:05

2 (a) 14:01   (b) 15:16

● Challenge
Variable answers

Measures

1 (a) 81.25 m   (b) 4.8 kg   (c) 63 m

2 (a) 3049 cm   (b) 40 days

● Challenge
24.75 kg of food is eaten by the teams.

Puzzles

1 (a) 24   (b) 301   (c) 122 and 123

2 (a) 18 and 81, 27 and 72, 36 and 63, 54 and 45
(b) 3

● Challenge
137

Patterns and sequences

1 (a) 2138, 2214 and 2290
(b) 1142, 1218 and 1294
(c) 990, 914 and 838

2 (a) 6
(b) If the current year is 2007, then the comet Denning-Fujikawa will have been seen 15 times including its first sighting.

● Challenge
Answers will vary.

Multiplication

1 (a) £248.30   (b) 13 kg   (c) £39

2 (a) £28,800   (b) £937.72

● Challenge
£179.40

Division

1 (a) 100 coach loads
  (b) £80
  (c) £45

2 (a) 6 minutes
  (b) £12.50

● Challenge
 £8,928.57

2D shapes

1 (a) 4

  (b) A trapezium

  (c) Equilateral triangle (3 sides),
    parallelogram (4 sides),
    irregular hexagon (6 sides)

2 (a) 12

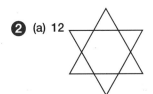

  (b) 24

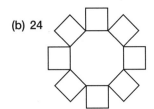

● Challenge

x	h	e	p	t	a	g	o	n	l	a	w	e	r	y
p	f	b	a	d	p	e	n	t	a	g	o	n	p	u
y	g	h	p	a	z	q	d	i	a	g	o	n	a	l
i	k	s	d	r	b	u	j	s	z	m	c	e	r	r
s	e	c	j	k	c	i	r	c	l	e	t	q	a	h
q	u	a	d	r	i	l	a	t	e	r	a	l	l	o
u	i	l	e	a	q	a	t	r	a	d	g	p	l	m
a	v	e	t	u	o	t	k	i	t	e	o	o	e	b
r	u	n	g	r	h	e	x	a	g	o	n	l	l	u
e	q	e	g	d	z	r	u	n	o	h	l	y	o	s
s	o	r	e	c	t	a	n	g	l	e	c	g	g	c
t	p	a	r	a	l	l	e	l	e	f	s	o	r	l
b	m	u	i	s	o	s	c	e	l	e	s	n	a	j
f	a	b	u	t	r	a	p	e	z	i	u	m	m	h

3D shapes

1

2

	At least one pair of parallel faces	No parallel faces
At least one pair of perpendicular edges	cube	square-based pyramid
No perpendicular edges	cylinder	tetrahedon

● Challenge

	Number of faces (F)	Number of vertices (V)	Number of edges (E)
Tetrahedron	4	4	6
Cube	6	8	12
Square-based pyramid	5	5	8
Triangular prism	5	6	9
Octahedron	8	6	12

Connection: $F + V = E - 2$

Position and direction

1 (a) (4, −4), (4, −6), (6, −4) and (6, −6)
  (b) Swimming (hopefully!)
  (c) (−6, 4), (−6, 6) and (−4, 6) or (4, 6), (6, 6) and (6, 4)

2 (a) (−2, −3), (−2, −1), (−5, −1) and (−5, 2)
  (b) (−4, −6), (−6, −6), (−6, −4) and (−4, −4)

● Challenge
 Answers will vary.

Data handling

1 (a) 1–10
  (b) 21–30
  (c) 20

2 (a) 44
  (b) 68

● Challenge
 Graph should show a bias towards the younger age brackets.

Two-step problems

1 (a) £54
  (b) £6.75
  (c) There are 68 sweets left. They made £15.32.

2 (a) 102 sponges were thrown
  (b) £28.50

● Challenge
 3 ducks